AROMATHERAPY
massage

hinkler

Margie Hare

Published by Hinkler Books Pty Ltd
45-55 Fairchild Street
Heatherton Victoria 3202 Australia
www.hinklerbooks.com

hinkler

Art Director: Karen Moores
Editors: Margaret Barca and Sofija Stefanovic
Design: Susie Allen and Hinkler Studio
Photographer: Glenn Weiss
Photo credits: Rosemary essential oil © Igordutina/Dreamstime.com,
Outdoor Massage © Eastwest Imaging/Dreamstime.com,
Spa Treatment © Kelly Cline/istockphoto.com
Special thanks to Mud Brick Herb Cottage
and also to Lee-Ann Dixon and Rock O'Keefe

ISBN 978 1 7418 5636 1

Printed and bound in China

CONTENTS

WHAT IS AROMATHERAPY MASSAGE?

Massage is a healing practice dating back to ancient times. The benefits of massage are widely known to be therapeutic on a physical, functional, and psychological level. Massage involves the manipulation of the body with pressure to the body's soft tissue. This book guides you through the unique healing combination of massage and aromatherapy.

The modern usage of the word "aromatherapie" originated with the French chemist René Maurice Gattefosse. In the 1920s he suffered burns to his arm and hand in a laboratory accident. He plunged his arm into a container of pure lavender essential oil, mistaking it for water. Despite third degree burns he made a speedy recovery with no scarring. He subsequently researched the properties of lavender that caused this recovery and passed his findings on to the medical profession.

When we use oils in massage, they are absorbed into the skin, and we use various techniques and oils depending on the needs of the individual being treated. Aromatherapy massage uses pure essential oils skilfully and in a controlled manner to influence mind, body, and soul for physical and emotional health and wellbeing.

When we "take time to smell the roses," there may be more to it than we think. Rose essential oil has many properties—it is an antidepressant, antiseptic, antispasmodic, antiviral, aphrodisiac, astringent, bactericide, laxative, sedative, and heart tonic, to mention a few.

Aromatherapy massage is used as a stimulating or relaxing therapy, to aid the penetration of essential oils into the body. In this book, you will be introduced to various strokes and techniques that will enable you to perform a full body aromatherapy massage.

THE HISTORY OF AROMATHERAPY

The use of plants, aromas, and natural ingredients for healing and improving health dates back thousands of years. Essential oils were used by the ancient civilizations of Egypt, China, the Middle East, India, and Greece.

In Egypt, exotic perfumes were used in abundance by the Pharaohs and their families.

Oils were used in embalming and in the temples they were used as offerings to the gods. The Greeks and the Romans were famous for the use of aromatic oils and massage in their bath houses. In the Middle East plants were used widely for their medicinal and therapeutic properties. Oils and aromatic medicines were brought to Europe from the Middle East by the crusaders. Aromatherapy developed during the Middle Ages in Europe into one of the most sought after forms of natural healing. In Asia the oldest form of Indian medicine is known as Ayurvedic, and an important aspect of this principle is massage with essential oils.

The author, Margie Hare

WHAT ARE ESSENTIAL OILS?

Essential oils occur widely in the plant kingdom and are sometimes referred to as the plants' "life force." They are minute drops of liquid occurring in glands, hairs, or veins of flowers, leaves, seeds, bark and wood, resin, roots, or fruit peel of the plant. They give the plant its very specific scent. These droplets are a mixture of complex, organic compounds. When extracted they are highly concentrated and volatile (which means that they turn quickly from a liquid into a gas at room temperature and higher). In lavender they occur in the flowering tops of lavender, in oranges in the peel, and in rosemary in the leaves. The most common form of extraction is by steam distillation.

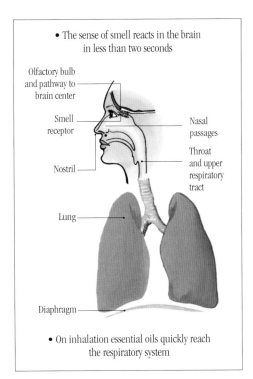

- The sense of smell reacts in the brain in less than two seconds

Olfactory bulb and pathway to brain center

Smell receptor

Nostril

Lung

Diaphragm

Nasal passages

Throat and upper respiratory tract

- On inhalation essential oils quickly reach the respiratory system

Main Camp Tea Tree Oil Distillation Plant, Northern NSW, Australia. Photo courtesy of TP Health Ltd, Ballina NSW, Australia.

How essential oils work

Essential oils enter the body by two main routes—the skin and the nose. They enter and leave the body efficiently, leaving no toxins behind. When inhaled, essential oils come into contact with the olfactory system located in the nose and behind the eyes. These oils are also absorbed easily through the pores and hair follicles in the skin. Essential oils are taken directly into the blood stream; they have a positive effect on blood circulation, helping to bring oxygen and nutrients to the tissues while assisting in the disposal of carbon dioxide and other waste materials.

I believe aromatherapy works in a holistic way, addressing the mind, body, and soul. The main benefits come from the pleasant fragrances, which have a positive psychological effect.

A selection of pure essential oils

GUIDELINES WHEN USING ESSENTIAL OILS

Essential oils are highly concentrated. It is important to follow the dosages recommended. More is not better. On the contrary, it can have an adverse effect. The difference in the effect between one drop and two drops can be substantial.

GENERAL CAUTIONS

- Do not take internally.
- Keep out of reach of children.
- Avoid using essential oils near eyes and other sensitive areas.
- Always read the precautions on the bottle before using.
- Use only 100% pure essential oils.
- Keep oils away from any naked flame.
- Store oils well sealed in a cool, dark place.
- Never use neat.

Some oils can increase the risk of sunburn

SPECIAL CAUTIONS

- Avoid the following essential oils during pregnancy: basil, cedar aurantiumwood, clary sage, clove bud, cypress, fennel, jasmine, juniper, lemongrass, marjoram, peppermint, rosemary, thyme.
- Do not use essential oils on newborn babies.
- Some oils can cause photo-sensitization of the skin, increasing the risk of sunburn. These include bergamot, ginger, lemon, lemon verbena, lime, mandarin, and orange.
- The following oils should not be used on sensitive skins: basil, fennel, lemongrass, lemon, lemon verbena, melissa, orange, peppermint, thyme.
- Avoid sage, thyme, cypress, and rosemary oil if there is any possibility of high blood pressure, epilepsy, or kidney disease.
- If having to drive a long distance after a massage, do not use clary sage, marjoram, or ylang ylang—they can cause drowsiness.
- If prone to epilepsy, do not use fennel, rosemary, or sage.

BENEFITS OF AROMATHERAPY MASSAGE

The purpose of aromatherapy massage is to aid the penetration of essential oils into the body and to treat problem areas. Massage can be stimulating or relaxing depending on the oils used and the technique applied.
It is an effective way to relieve stress, anxiety, and tension. Aromatherapy massage combines the balancing properties of the essential oils with the relaxing benefits of touch. As the oils are absorbed into the skin and the muscles relax, the therapeutic benefits manifest. Psychologically, massage promotes a wonderful feeling of lightness and wellbeing. Massage is a valuable gift to give a friend—it not only soothes the mind and body but it has numerous other benefits. A good aromatherapy massage will:

- increase metabolism
- speed up the healing process
- enhance the removal of toxins
- increase muscle and joint mobility
- improve skin tone
- aid relaxation by calming the nervous system
- improve circulation of blood and lymph
- relieve mental and physical tiredness
- reduce aches, pains, spasms, and stiffness
- improve digestion.

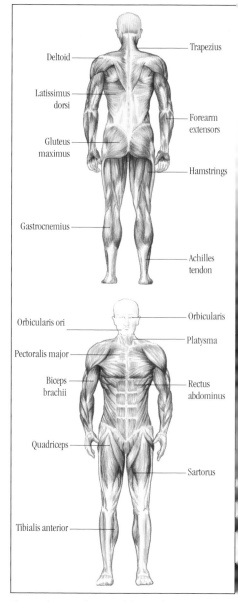

The muscle system: be aware of the muscle structure as you massage. Muscles become more flexible and muscle tension and cramps are reduced during massage.

GETTING STARTED

This book is not intended to enable you to treat the public professionally or to replace your medical practitioner. It is intended to give you the confidence to use essential oils safely, have fun, treat your friends and family, and enjoy the wonderful benefits of aromatherapy in the home. Treat simple everyday ailments, but if they persist or become severe, seek professional help.

MEASUREMENTS

Useful information when working with essential oils:

- 20 drops = 1 ml essential oil
- 1 ml essential oil = 1 cc
- 10 ml bottle contains 200 drops
- 100 drops = 1 teaspoon = 5 cc

ESSENTIALS IN YOUR STARTER KIT

- stainless steel/enamel/china footbath
- 1 box Epsom/Dead Sea salts
- 1 bottle sweet almond carrier oil
- 9 essential oils: lavender, tea tree, peppermint, chamomile, eucalyptus, geranium, rosemary, lemon, orange
- 1 jar vegetable base cream
- glass measuring cylinder
- stainless steel stirrer
- selection of empty dark glass bottles and jars

YOU WILL ALSO NEED THE FOLLOWING ITEMS FROM THE KITCHEN OR BATHROOM:

- stainless steel mixing bowls and whisk
- a teaspoon and a tablespoon measure
- tissues
- spatula
- bottled spring/filtered water
- whole milk/cream/powdered goats' milk
- glycerin
- hot water bottle
- towels
- paper towel
- cottonwool, cleansing pads, and cottonbuds
- nip of vodka
- honey
- rice flour or cornstarch
- blank labels

AROMATHERAPY MASSAGE

PREPARING FOR A MASSAGE

PREPARE YOURSELF

- Be sure your nails are short and clean
- Wear comfortable clothes
- Remove all jewelry
- Wash hands before each massage
- Drink a full glass of filtered or spring water

MAKE SURE YOU HAVE EVERYTHING TO HAND SO THERE ARE NO INTERRUPTIONS

- A futon, a yoga mat, or a large spongy mat on the floor is fine
- A small table close at hand
- Carrier oil and pure essential oil mix in a bowl
- Basin of boiling water to warm small bowl of mixed oil
- Enough towels—bath sheets and smaller towels
- Eye bag
- Box of tissues
- Three pillows
- A head rest
- Heater to warm the towels
- An essential oil-warmer burning with relaxing essential oils

- Have a hot water bottle handy for under the feet
- Have a glass of water to offer the person you are massaging

SET THE MOOD FOR A SNUG, COMFORTABLE, AND RELAXED ENVIRONMENT

- Make sure there is no draft
- In cold weather heat the room
- Ensure dim lighting—no bright overhead lights
- Play soft, soothing music
- Unplug the phones or put on silent and switch off cell phones
- Put note on door— DO NOT DISTURB

MENTAL PREPARATION

As you prepare the room, light the candle burner and add the oils to clear any negative energy that might be in the area. Take a deep breath, relax for a few minutes, concentrate on your breathing. As you breathe in visualize taking in heaps of clean oxygenated air. As you breathe out visualize your muscles relaxing as you expel the carbon dioxide with all your "stuff" of the day. Visualize it leaving your body and being dispelled by the burning light of the candle. Visualize putting any pressing problems you have into a drawer and closing it, leaving your mind relaxed and present in the moment for the massage.

AROMATHERAPY MASSAGE SEQUENCE

INTRODUCTION

There are various different strokes and techniques used in massage. In this sequence you will learn opening and closing techniques, effleurage, kneading, stroking thumbs/finger circles, sweeping, fanning, circling movements, the figure of 8, percussion, stretching, the corkscrew, finger press, and pinching.

Begin by connecting with your subject and becoming fully aware of your breathing. This is done with your subject fully covered with towels.

1. Effleurage

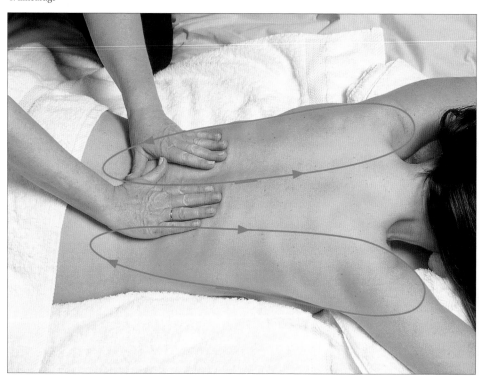

Position yourself at your subject's side. With your hands above their body as you clear your thoughts, relax, breathe, and begin to feel the energy flowing into your hands as you breathe in. Place one hand at the base of the spine and the other at the top of the spine. Rest for a moment. Note any sensations or impressions.

Ask your subject to breathe in and out three times using deep abdominal breathing. This helps your subject to let go and slow their mind and body.

Without losing contact with the body, position yourself at the subject's head and gently rest your fingers on their hairline as they breathe in. Ask them to breathe in again and to visualize any 'stuff' coming up for them that they need to let go of. As they breathe out, drag your fingers like a rake through their hair and flick off at the end of their hair. Rake through their hair with your fingers three times. You are now ready to begin the full body massage.

BACK AND BUTTOCKS

Effleurage is a gentle, fan-like stroke used at the beginning of the massage. It helps to spread the oil over the skin, relaxing the surface of the skin.

This stroke uses the palm of the hand, with fingers and wrists relaxed. The movements feel smooth and rhythmic. Effleurage can be done at any point through the massage to connect different strokes.

EFFLEURAGE

1. Gently fold the towel down the back to the middle of the buttocks. Pour just enough oil into your palms, rub hands together, position yourself at the lower back, facing the body. Slowly slide both hands up the spine to the neck. Fan both hands over each shoulder, cupping and embracing the upper arm as you slide your hands to the underarm position, then slowly slide lightly down the sides of the body to the starting position. Repeat rhythmically several times until the oil is well spread. The slow rhythmic movement of this stroke is deeply relaxing.

KNEADING

This is a medium-pressure stroke. It is used after the muscles have been relaxed and oil has been spread over the skin. This technique is like kneading dough. You will be working more deeply to further relax the muscles, release general tension, and increase circulation. Place hands flat, fingers together with thumbs stretched out wide. Using your thumb to push in, squeeze and pinch the flesh toward the fingers, scooping up the skin. The hands work alternately, pressing and squeezing the muscles in a rolling movement. Kneading speeds up blood and lymph flow.

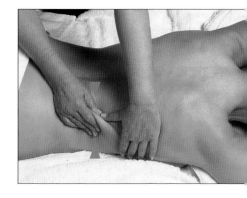

2. Position yourself square to the body.
Lean across and press into the opposite buttock with your thumbs spread wide as they roll toward the fingers of the same hand. Work your hands in a rhythmic movement, alternately up the side, from the sacrum, across over hip joint, up the side of the ribs in a rhythmic movement, working upward toward the shoulder. This can be a very tense and painful area so work sensitively. Work in two rows, buttock to shoulder, on both sides of the spine.

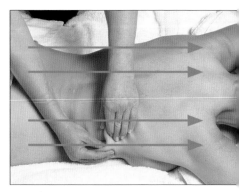

2. Kneading

THUMB CIRCLES

Make small rhythmic circles with your thumb or fingertips. As you circle, the pressure continues downwards. Always check your pressure is causing no discomfort or pain. When you come across a knot, gently work through it, increasing pressure as it releases. To relax a muscle, begin pressure, gently increasing it when you feel a response. Continue circling the area a few times and then move on, so as not to cause resistance or irritation.

3. Position yourself at your subject's lower back. Work with both thumbs alongside each other at the same time. Perform small continuous circles from the sacrum to the base of the skull three times on each side of the spine.

Cautions Do not work *on* the spine—work on either side of the vertebrae.

3. Thumb circles

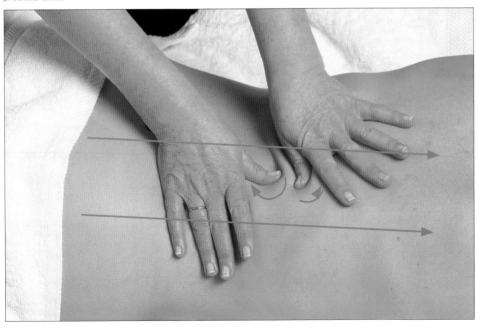

Stroking

This is the simplest movement, with palms down and hands flat (on large areas) and curved (around small areas). It is one of the gentle light-pressure techniques. You can do it with your fingers only, or you can cat stroke: one hand follows the other and curves so only the fingertips touch at the end of the stroke. It can be performed at the end of massage sequences. Stroking is pleasurable and connects sensations to the area that has just been massaged. It draws attention to that part of the body, relaxing, revitalizing, and stimulating the skin. When performed slowly, it has a calming and soothing effect. When performed with fast rapid strokes, it is invigorating.

4. Position yourself square to the body with flat hands, straight fingers, stroke away from you from the middle of the spine to the side of the body. Start at the shoulder and finish at the hips and back again. Repeat on the other side of the spine, stroking toward you. Begin at the shoulder. Alternatively, position yourself at the head, reach to the lower back, place one hand on the sacrum, and cat stroke with alternating hands all the way up the spine to the skull. Repeat three times.

Sweeping

This is a light to medium stroke using the palm and fingers held flat. It is used after squeezing the muscles to relax, stretch and open them out. The strokes are worked in quick succession, one hand after the other, with pressure away from the spine when working the back and hip area.

5. Position yourself at the hip and lightly place your hands on the far side of the hip and buttock. Sweep hands alternately one after the other in a downward movement away from you toward the side of the body. Repeat the stroke, moving slowly toward the shoulder with each sweep. Repeat from buttock to shoulder again. Repeat on the other side.

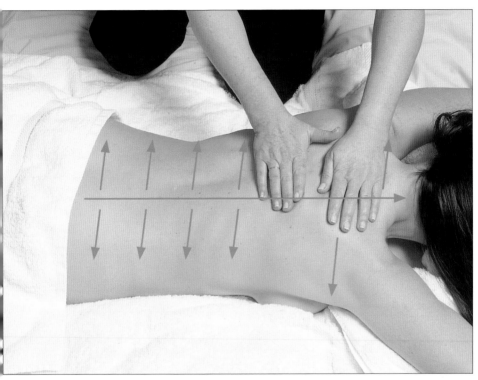

4. Stroking

FANNING

Is a light to medium stroke performed with flat hands and straight fingers. Palms of your hands should pivot as fingers fan over the body.

6. Position yourself at the side of your subject with flat hands placed on the shoulder. The first stroke applies firm downward pressure. You lighten the pressure as you fan over the shoulder and continue with alternating hands down the spine, fanning outward to the side and moving downward to the hip. Repeat on the other side.

CIRCLING OVER BUTTOCKS

Here your hands are in the same position as for stroking, only they move in circles. You place one hand on the other, palms down and make one single circle. This stroke is very comforting and relaxing.

7. Position yourself at the hip area. Place both hands gently and flat, one on top of the other, in the middle of the opposite buttock. Use gentle pressure in slow, rhythmic circles several times.

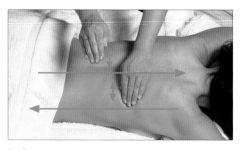

8a. Cupping

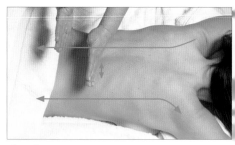

8b. Hacking

PERCUSSION

This is a series of three strokes— cupping, hacking, and pummeling. Work from the buttocks to the shoulder and back, one hand following the other in rapid succession. The movements are brisk with firm pressure. Work up one side and down the other.

8a. Cupping: cup your hand forming a vacuum in the palm of your hand, fingers straight, and thumb pulled tight in. As you cup the skin with one hand flick off immediately, do the same with the other hand.

8b. Hacking: hold hands straight with palms facing. Hack the skin with the sides of your hands, one hand following the other. As your hand touches the skin bounce off immediately.

8c. Pummeling: form an open fist closing the top with your thumb. Pummel the skin briskly, bouncing off on contact, alternating each hand in rhythmic succession.

Cautions Take care not to strike delicate areas—work on muscles either side of spine—see the muscle chart, page 10.

8c. Pummeling

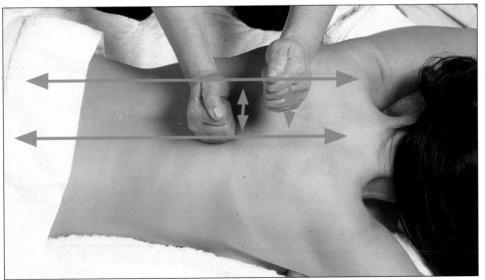

FIGURE OF 8

The number 8 represents infinity. It is considered the most active spiritual number, the number of wisdom, being intuition expressed through loving action. This technique is similar to circling but in a figure of 8, with both hands working at the same time in opposite directions. The pressure is medium to firm. It is used near the end of massaging a body part, when the area is warm and relaxed. Use varying pressure during the stroke. As you go over bony parts, the pressure is light, while over the muscle you can increase the pressure.

9. Position yourself at one side of your subject, starting with one hand on either side of the buttock. Move the hands with firm pressure as you circle in opposite directions and cross at the sacrum. Move smoothly up the back, repeating three figures of 8 in each position, until you finish with a set of figure of 8 across the shoulders.

9. Figure of 8

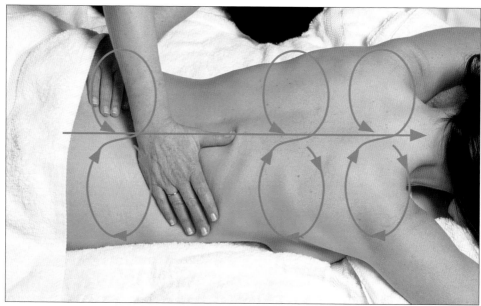

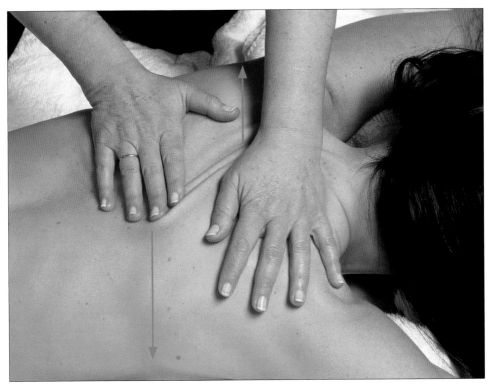

10. Wringing

WRINGING

This stroke is done criss-crossing from side to side firmly. This creates warm friction on muscle fibre.

10. Work from hips to shoulder blade and back again three times. For complete relaxation work slowly. For an invigorating effect speed up the tempo. Continuously stroke your hands in opposite directions as you wring the entire back region.

STRETCHING

This stroke has a firm, very slow, downward pressure of the hands, palms flat (abdomen, arms, and legs), palms facing each other (back), while sliding hands apart diagonally in opposite directions. You can also turn them in opposite directions to twist and wring as you stretch. On the abdomen, the pressure should be medium, not firm. This stroke gives the body a sense of opening out and not being held in.

11. Face your subject and position yourself at their waist. Bring your palms together, then place them in the middle of the back on the spine. Place pressure on the muscles on either side of the spine but not on the vertebrae. Slowly, very slowly with firm pressure, draw the hands apart feeling the muscle move beneath the side edge of your hands. If you do not feel it, you are moving too fast. Slide in opposite directions, one hand to the sacrum the other to the top of the neck. Hold the finish for a few seconds with firm pressure. Lift and place hands quickly once again in the middle of the back on the spine, and slide one hand to the hip and the other to the shoulder. Repeat, moving the hands to the opposite hip and shoulder.

To finish the back and buttocks

Complete three, rhythmic effleurage strokes. The first medium pressure, the second light pressure and slowing in pace, the last featherlight and very slow.

Draping—bring the towel back and cover the body completely. Rest one hand on the towel at the top of the spine and the other hand at the base of the spine as you connect with your subject. Rest for a few seconds. You are now ready to start the arms. Fold corner of towel exposing entire arm and shoulder area.

1. Effleurage of the arms

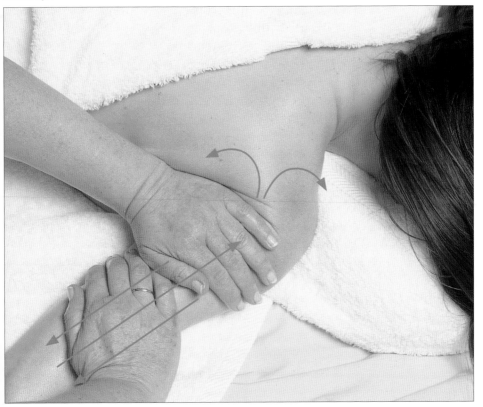

ARMS

1. Uncover one arm. Effleurage the arm from hand to shoulder three times as you apply oil.

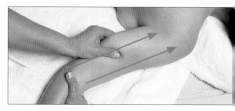
2. Knead upper arm

2. Knead upper arm with a sliding movement, applying pressure with the thumbs. Repeat three times on the inside and three times on the outside. Supporting the arm, complete three hand circles on the elbow with a flat palm and pressure on the inside of the elbow. Knead the lower arm three times with pressure on the inside of wrists.

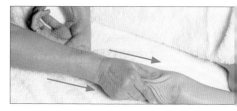
2. Knead lower arm

3. Do knuckle circles into the palm of the hand.

CORKSCREW OFF EACH FINGER

This is a gentle but firm sliding, twisting, and pulling stroke. It can be done on fingers and toes.

4. Hold the subject's hand at the wrist, with your other hand. Curl all four fingers of your hand around each finger one at a time. Twist gently as you slide off each finger starting with the thumb. Twist off each finger pulling gently as you slide off. Finish with the little finger.

5. Three effleurage strokes up the arm to finish. Firm, lighter, and fairy lightness to finish. Repeat all five steps on the other arm.

To complete massaging this side of the body: place one hand on the neck and the other at the base of the spine. Hold for a few seconds and visualize your subject completely relaxed. Lift the towel to screen your face and ask your subject to turn over. For comfort, place a pillow under the knees. Offer your subject an eye pad to assist relaxation. Place support under the neck if necessary. Ask if they are warm enough. You are now ready to massage the front of the body.

3. Knuckle circling

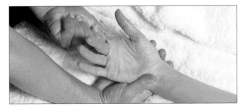

4. Corkscrew off each finger

5. Three effleurage strokes up the arm to finish

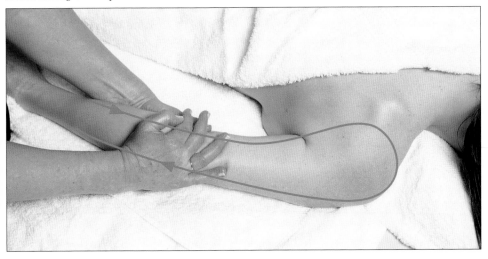

FRONT AND BACK OF LEGS

1. Effleurage the full front of the leg three times as you apply oil. First on the lower leg, then either side of the knee, then the upper leg.

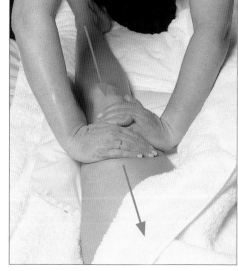

2. Knead the upper front leg then the lower front leg. Three times each in three lines. Use very light sliding pressure on shin bone.

3. Run finger circles around each side of the ankle. This is the same as the thumb circle but using one, two, or three fingers. Complete three circles, working both hands on either side of the ankle at the same time.

1. Effleurage of the front of the leg three times as you apply oil

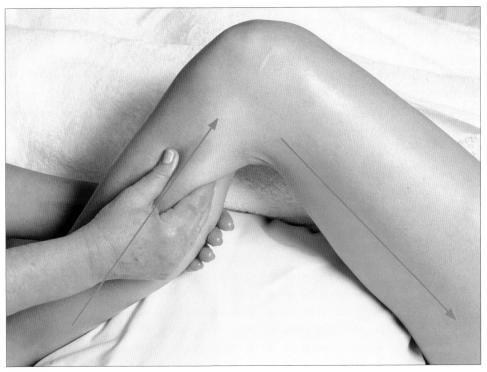

5. Knead the back of the leg

4. Gently slide one hand under the knee, the other hand on ankle. Push ankle while lifting the knee into a 45° angle and secure foot with corner of towel. Use more oil if necessary using effleurage stroke.

5. First knead the calf and through the thigh. Work both sides of the leg three times each, first on the lower leg, and then on the upper leg.

KNEES, ANKLES, FEET

6. Complete circles around the knee with palm and finger. Both hands following each other.

7. Do finger circles around each side of the ankle. Hold the ankle between your wrists and gently rock from side to side three times.

8. Foot stretch. Slide both hands around the foot and stretch the top of the foot with thumbs facing up. Slide firmly to the outside of the foot while fingers are exerting pressure into the solar plexus. Repeat three times.

9. Toe circles. Hold each toe one at a time, gently circle clockwise then anticlockwise and corkscrew off. Move to the next toe until all toes are massaged.

10. Foot twist. Place one hand on the inside of the foot and the other hand on the outside of the foot. Using the heels of the hand pull the outside of the foot towards you with one hand as you push the inside of the foot away from you and visa versa. Work along the edges of the foot from the heels to the toes and back again three times. This technique loosens the lower back, upper back, and shoulders.

To finish, effleurage from toe to thigh three times. The first time apply medium pressure, the second time light pressure and slowing in pace, the last time featherlight and very slowly. Hold both your hands still on the foot for a few seconds. Visualize all tension leaving the entire body. Cover and repeat on the other leg. Repeat step 1–10 on the other leg.

7. Finger circles on the ankle

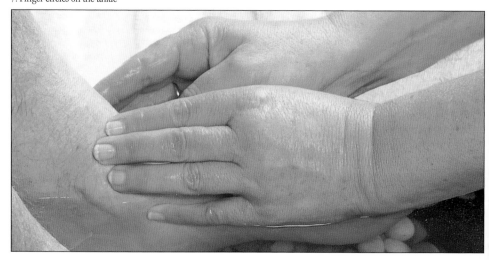

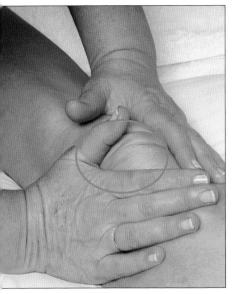

6. Hand circles

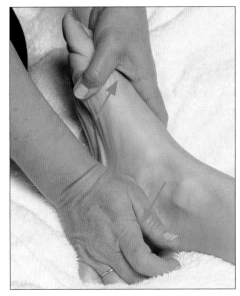

8. Foot stretch

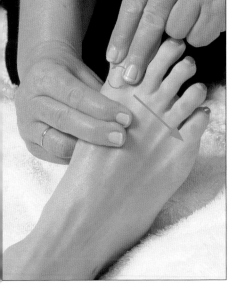

9. Toe circles

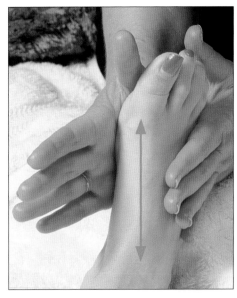

10. Foot twist

Abdomen

Drape the chest with a towel (for women). Fold a towel in half lengthwise and place half over one shoulder, make a "V" over the breast area and fold the other half over the other shoulder. Pull the towel covering the breast area down to hips while securing the "V" towel in place. Position yourself at the right side of your subject.

1. Effleurage the abdomen in clockwise circles. Apply the oil with flat hands. Starting in a small circle, very gently apply pressure and make larger and larger circles. Repeat several times. This is a very calming technique.

2. Place hands, palms flat, on the abdomen below the navel. Rest there for a few seconds, tuning into your subject's breathing. As your subject breathes out, apply gentle pressure with the flat of your hands. Draw your hands apart, sliding toward the hips. Stretch outwards. Do not dig in. Gently tuck hands under the hips, lift slightly, and rock gently from side to side.

1. Effleurage

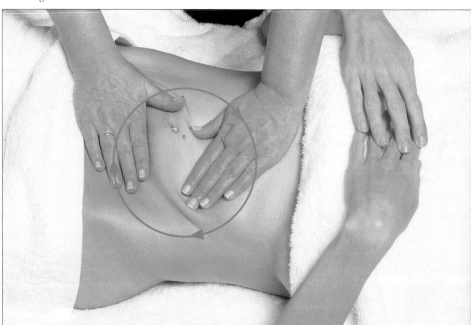

Repeat three times. Should your subject have a navel ring slightly cup your hands. Rest the hands there for the count of three as you tune in. Then, very slowly, move both hands in slow, rhythmic, and continuous circles, starting with a very small circle over the navel. Repeat these circles, moving clockwise, making larger circles until you are covering the entire tummy area. Do many large circles before you start to go smaller and finish in the starting position. Hold that position for the count of 20.

3. To finish, place the right hand flat on solar plexus (between ribs). With very gentle pressure, circle five times very slowly in a clockwise direction, hold for a few seconds and remove. Replace drape. Fold both top ends of the "V" back over chest exposing both shoulders, top of the chest, and neck area.

3. Solar plexus

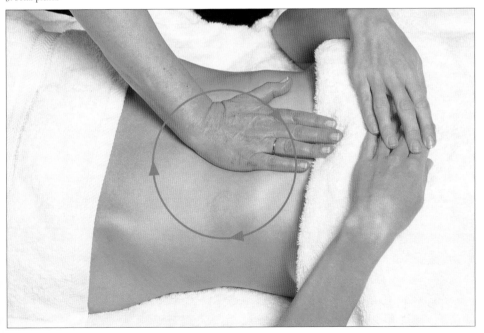

CHEST, NECK, AND SHOULDERS

1. Stand at your subject's head.
Effleurage the entire area with oil, starting with both hands in the middle of the chest; slide over shoulders, behind the neck, and slowly up the back of the neck, taking in the ears with your fingers and then sliding gently off under the head and the hair. Repeat three times slowly and rhythmically.

2. Finger press. Place both hands in the middle of the chest, fingers resting between the ribs. Press slowly and evenly between the top ribs, starting in the center and moving outward. Apply firm pressure and hold for a few seconds. Slide along between ribs and press again. Repeat three times. Be careful not to put pressure on breast tissue. This step stimulates the neurolymphatic reflex points. Repeat with thumbs only, in two positions at the armpit.

3. Shoulder press. With one hand on left shoulder and one on the right gently press right shoulder down; then press left shoulder, then together. Repeat three times. Always work rhythmically.

4. Shoulder effleurage with flat hands.
Work both hands together from shoulder to shoulder and back again three times.

5. Effleurage the neck starting in the middle of the chest. Move outward to the shoulder and end with both hands underneath the neck with your fingers at either side of the spine. Make small finger circles inward to the neck and repeat three times. Support the head with one hand and gently turn the head to the left. Effleurage from the shoulder up the back of the neck to hairline. Firmly massage scalp from base of skull to top of head with fingers spread wide. Move the scalp not the hair. Supporting the head, gently turn to other side and repeat. This stimulating action on the scalp improves circulation, increases blood flow, nourishes the hair follicles, and stimulates nerve endings. You are now ready to start massaging the face.

1. Effleurage starting on chest

1. Effleurage complete by sliding under head and off hair

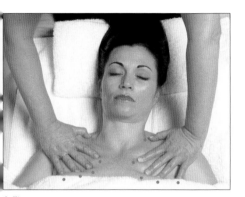

2. Finger press

3. Shoulder press

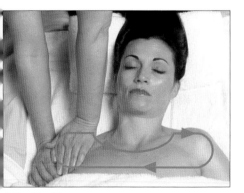

4. Shoulder effleurage

5. Final effleurage and scalp massage

4. Lower lip

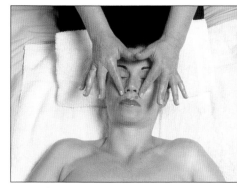

5. Sinus finger press

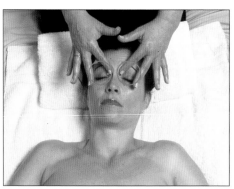

6. Eye circles

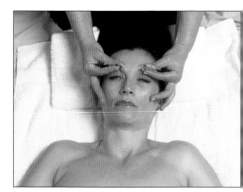

7. Eyebrow pinch

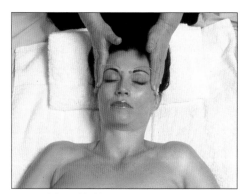

8. Press, slide, and hold

Finish—rake the hair

FACE

1. Using the palms of the hand, effleurage the entire face with oil, with both hands mirroring each other. Work gentle strokes with fingertips from forehead to chin, over nose, and with care around the eyes.

2. Place the heel of your hands on the forehead. Stroke rhythmically outward toward the temples. Hold and release. Repeat three times.

3. Massage the chin. Use sideways movements from the middle of the chin, along the jaw bone, to under the ears with fingers underneath and thumbs working in circles. Pat gently under jaw line with the ring and middle fingers in a bouncing percussion movement.

4. Gently press five times below the lower lip using your middle three finger pads. Repeat on the upper lip. This helps to relax the jaw.

5. Gently press five times on acupressure point at the side of nose using your pointer finger pads. This is used to relieve sinus problems.

6. With your pointer finger, draw up from the base of the nose to under the eyebrow. Apply gentle finger press three times then glide three times along the eyebrow circle over the temple and back under the eyes to the nose. This is amazingly relaxing, relieving all anxiety and tension.

7. Using your thumb and forefinger gently pinch firmly five times along the eyebrow. This technique relieves eyestrain and sinus congestion. Repeat three times.

8. Place your thumbs together on the forehead above the brows. Start at the third eye (between the eyebrows). Press lightly down, hold, release. Then stroke out across the forehead to the temples with pads and fingers and hold. Repeat this press, slide, and hold stroke three times. The slower and more even the pressure, the more effective the stroke. The movement should be delicate as if drawing tension away from the center of the face **To finish.** Massage the scalp all over with firm finger circles. Move the scalp. Do not slide on the hair. Now, rake the head in three lines starting at the hairline—very slowly with stiff, rake-like fingers glide from hairline all the way along the scalp and off the ends of the hair, flicking off as you finish. This cleansing action draws negative energy from the head and the hair. Complete the massage with a final effleurage over the chest, shoulders, up the back of the neck, include the ears, and off the hair. Repeat three times, getting slower and lighter each time. Finish with your thumbs gently positioned on the crown of the head, gently moving on the spot up and down for several moves. Cover your subject. Replace the eye bag. End the treatment by placing the palms of your hands on the soles of their feet for at least 10 seconds. This re-balances the flow of energy. Leave your subject for five minutes to allow the energy to settle. Wash your hands. Come back with a glass of water. Ask them to keep their eyes closed and take a deep breath in as you gently spritz their face. Repeat three times.

Pulse point massage

Add one drop of lavender pure essential oil to 1 ml carrier oil for headache relief.

Blend oil, then use your pointer and middle finger on each pulse point to massage into the four pulse points—at wrist, upper arm, on the neck at jugular vein, and at the temples.

Technique: apply pressure on point, hold for the count of three. Complete three small circles clockwise and three circles anticlockwise, then hold for the count of three. Move to the next pulse point. It is important to drink one glass of water before you start and one glass of water when you are finished.

Drink 2 liters of water over the next 24 hours. Try to maintain this level of water every day (about 8 cups). This is an easy, quick way to enable essential oils to enter the bloodstream and can be used successfully to treat problems such as headaches, insomnia, lack of concentration, and cold and flu.

Friction rub massage

Place a small amount of the blended oil in the palm of your hand and rub both hands together fast until they warm up. Take three deep breaths of the oil to assist sleep. You can friction rub children's feet to calm them at sleep time.

Pulse point massage on temples

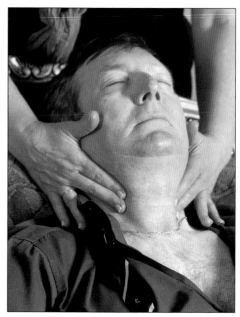

Pulse point massage on jugular vein

Pulse point massage on wrist

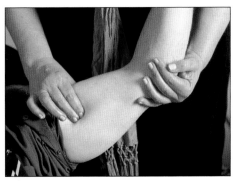

Pulse point massage on upper arm

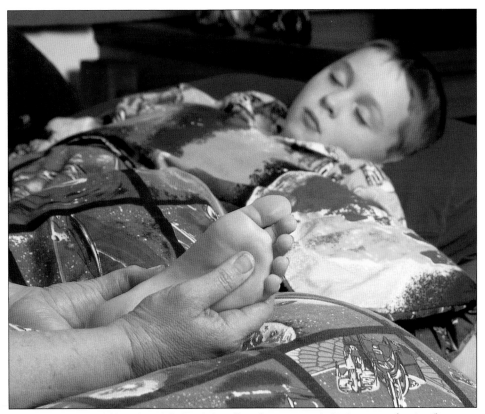

Friction rub or massage children's feet to help sleep (1 drop of lavender pure essential oil in 2 teaspoons of carrier oil)

POPULAR AROMATHERAPY OILS

Essential oils are derived from leaves, flowers, roots, the peel of certain fruits, and other parts of aromatic plants. Hundreds of plants have been used over the centuries for medicinal and therapeutic purposes and for general well-being. Modern aromatherapy uses a more limited selection, though their effects are wide-ranging.

This is not a complete reference for all essential oils, but is a selection of some of the most popular and safest oils for home use. Study the guide and refer to it before using your essential oils. In particular, be aware of any special cautions advised.

BASIL

THE APHRODISIAC OIL

Botanical name *Ocimum basilicum*

Plant part used Flowering sweet basil tops and leaves.

Main benefits Used for nervous insomnia, anxiety, and tiredness. Helpful for insect bites, headaches, muscular aches and pains.

Blending suggestions Blends well with eucalyptus, frankincense, geranium, ginger, lavender, lemon, rosemary, peppermint, pine, thyme, and tea tree.

My comment Use in hair conditioning treatment.

Cautions Avoid during pregnancy. Use with caution on sensitive skin as it can be an irritant.

Use as a hair conditioning treatment

BERGAMOT
THE UPLIFTING OIL

Botanical name
Citrus aurantium

Plant part used
Peel of the bitter orange.

Main benefits Good for relaxing tight, aching muscles.

Blending suggestions For massage, bergamot is extremely versatile and can lift any blend. Try it with marjoram, jasmine, and rose or sandalwood.

My comment Try bergamot neat on cold sores as well as in uplifting body freshening spray.

Cautions Do not use when going in the sun.

CEDARWOOD (ATLAS)
A REFRESHING OIL FOR MEN

Botanical name *Cedrus atlantica*

Main benefits This oil has a stimulating, refreshing, and tonic effect on the body. It is good for dandruff, eczema, greasy skin, and acne. It is an effective insect repellent.

Blending suggestions This oil blends well with bergamot, cypress, frankincense, juniper, lavender, rosemary, and lemon.

My comment Use for athlete's foot.

Cautions Avoid during pregnancy. This oil should be avoided by breast-feeding mothers and by children.

CHAMOMILE (ROMAN)
THE SOOTHING OIL

Botanical name
Chamaemelum nobile

Plant part used
Freshly dried flowers.

Main benefits This oil is a natural anti-inflammatory with great healing properties as well as relaxing sedative benefits.

Blending suggestions Chamomile is an expensive oil and you can substitute some drops with lavender when using to ease pain. Blends well with geranium, lavender, patchouli, and rose.

My comment Safe for use on babies, children, and pets.

CLARY SAGE
THE ANTIDEPRESSANT OIL

Botanical name
Salvia sclarea

Plant part used
Leaves and flowers.

Main benefits
Calming, promotes a peaceful state of mind and restful sleep, improves mental clarity and alertness, and reduces stress and tension.

Blending suggestions Blends well with cedarwood, geranium, juniper, lavender, and sandalwood.

My comment Use in massage oil blend for varicose veins.

Cautions This essential oil should not be used in large doses, as it can be stupefying. Clary sage is well known for its euphoric action. Not to be used during pregnancy.

EUCALYPTUS
THE PERFECT INSECT REPELLENT

Botanical name
Eucalyptus globulus

Plant part used
Fresh leaves and twigs.

Main benefits Because
eucalyptus oil prevents bacterial growth
and inhibits the growth of viruses it is
used to treat burns, blisters, cuts, herpes,
wounds, and sores. Has been used
for centuries by Australian Aboriginal
communities for healing wounds.
Added to massage oil, cream, and baths
it soothes the pain of sore muscles,
arthritis, and rheumatism.

Blending suggestions The clean
camphor-like perfume of eucalyptus
blends well with lavender, rosemary,
tea tree, and pine.

My comment Gargle and steam
inhalation for sore throats and
persistent coughs.

Cautions Avoid using this oil if
suffering from high blood pressure
or epilepsy. Do not use this oil while
on homoeopathic remedies—it could
negate the healing effect. Do not take
internally.

GERANIUM
THE WOMEN'S OIL

Botanical name
Pelargonium graveolens

Plant part used
Leaves and flowers.

Main benefits Geranium oil has a
regulatory action on the hormones
secreted by the adrenal cortex. Ideal for
PMT and menopause. It reduces stress
and tension, is calming and uplifting,
speeds body healing, eases depression,
and is helpful in managing asthma. It
also acts as a tonic and diuretic on the
urinary system and the liver, which
helps rid the body of toxins.

Blending suggestions Geranium's
relaxing, rose-scented, heady aroma
blends well and balances most other
fragrances.

My comment Use in a massage blend
to help reduce cellulite deposits.

Cautions Dilute further than standard
dosage on sensitive skins as it may
cause irritation. Avoid long-term use
with history of oestrogen-dependant
cancer.

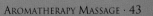

GINGER
THE WARMING OIL

Botanical name
Zingiber officinale

Plant part used Rhizome.

Main benefits A warming oil that relaxes tight muscles, relieves aches and pains, making it a natural choice to treat arthritis. Useful in the treatment of cold and coughs. Also improves digestion as it stimulates the gastric juices.

Blending suggestions The rich, spicy perfume of ginger blends well with lavender, lemon, grapefruit, orange, and petitgrain.

My comment Try as a chest rub for the winter chills.

Cautions Do not use on open skin. May cause irritation. Do not use within 72 hours of going into the sun.

GRAPEFRUIT
THE CELLULITE OIL

Botanical name
Citrus paradisi

Plant part used
Fruit rind.

Main benefits This oil has an uplifting and reviving effect, making it useful in treating stress, depression, and nervous exhaustion. Grapefruit is a lymphatic stimulant, so it is helpful in the treatment of water retention as well as having fat-dissolving properties.

Blending suggestions This fresh, sweet citrus aroma blends well with basil, bergamot, cedarwood, ginger, lime, lavender, rosemary, and ylang ylang.

Cautions A very safe oil to use. It is non-toxic, non-irritant, and will not make the skin sensitive to the sun.

JASMINE
THE ROMANTIC OIL

Botanical name
Jasminum grandiflorum

Plant part used
Fresh flowers.

Main benefits Uplifting, relaxing, and an excellent brain stimulant. It is good for dry sensitive skin and to treat muscular aches and menstrual cramps.

Blending suggestions This exotic, rich aroma blends well with lavender, orange, mandarin, neroli, rose, rosewood, and sandalwood.

My comment Always use this oil to lighten the emotional load.

Cautions Non-toxic, non-irritant. Not to be used during pregnancy.

LAVENDER
ESSENTIAL OIL FOR THE FIRST AID KIT

Botanical name
Lavandula angustifolia

Plant part used
Fresh flowers.

Main benefits Lavender is well known for its sedative properties and is useful in treating depression, migraine, insomnia, and nervous tension as well as dealing with stress.

Blending suggestions The floral, sweet scent of lavender blends well with bergamot, clary sage, lemon, mandarin, orange, pine, rosemary, and ylang ylang.

My comment Use neat on burns and even sunburn.

Cautions Non-toxic, non-irritant. Not suitable for very young children.

LEMON
THE CLEANSING OIL

Botanical name *Citrus limon*

Plant part used Rind of fruit.

Main benefits Lemon is stimulating, invigorating, astringent, deodorizing, and antiseptic. Very helpful in treating mental exhaustion. Also for energizing an aching body. Used in the treatment of cellulite.

Blending suggestions The tangy, fresh citrus aroma blends with bergamot, eucalyptus, frankincense, ginger, juniper, lavender, rose, and rosemary.

My comment Use in facial steam for normal skin.

Cautions Do not use this oil within 72 hours of going into the sun.

LEMONGRASS
THE REGENERATIVE OIL

Botanical name
Cymbopogon flexuosus

Plant part used Fresh and partially dried fronds.

Main benefits A good tonic for the skin, especially useful for athlete's foot. Lemongrass kills bacteria and fungal infections. It cools and reduces fever in the body and helps ease aching muscles. Lemongrass calms the nervous system relieving depression, stress, and nervous exhaustion.

Blending suggestions The warm, lemon, grassy aroma blends well with cedarwood, geranium, jasmine, lavender, neroli, rosemary, and tea tree.

My comment Good oil for fungal infections.

Cautions Use with care on sensitive skins—it can cause irritation due to high citrus content. Not suitable for toddlers. Halve the adult dilution as recommended for all topical applications. Use only 3 drops in the bath. Not to be used during pregnancy.

LIME

THE UPLIFTING OIL

Botanical name
Citrus aurantifolia

Plant part used
Fruit peel.

Main benefits This oil is antibacterial, antifungal, and antiseptic. A great stimulant and tonic. Very useful for treating colds and flu, cellulite, poor circulation, greasy skin, arthritis, and varicose veins.

Blending suggestions The sweet, fresh fragrance of the lime blends well with bergamot, cedarwood, geranium, grapefruit, lavender, lemon, mandarin, neroli, orange, rosemary, vetiver, and ylang ylang.

My comment Uplifting oil for bath and massage when feeling tired.

Cautions Can cause sensitivity. This oil is photo-sensitive. Do not use within 72 hours of going into the sun.

MANDARIN

THE CHILDREN'S OIL

Botanical name
Citrus reticulata

Plant part used
Fruit peel.

Main benefits
Having great digestive properties, it relieves cramps, spasms, and stimulates bile production. It also aids digestion, constipation, and hiccups. A great oil to use for stretch marks, scars, and aging skin.

Blending suggestions The citrus, sweet floral perfume of lime blends well with basil, bergamot, chamomile, grapefruit, lavender, lemon, neroli, orange, petitgrain, and rose.

My comment Use this oil during pregnancy to help reduce stretch marks.

Cautions Non-toxic and non-irritant. This oil can be photo-sensitive. Do not use within 72 hours of going in the sun.

MARJORAM
THE CALMING OIL

Botanical name
Origanum majorana

Plant part used Flowering tops and leaves.

Main benefits Marjoram relieves tight muscles, aches and pains, reduces inflammation, improves digestion, and helps relieve congestion.

Blending suggestions The woody, spicy, and camphor-like aroma blends well with bergamot, cedarwood, chamomile, clary sage, cypress, eucalyptus, juniper, lavender, mandarin, patchouli, rosemary, and tea tree.

My comment Use in bath and massage oil to calm and sedate.

Cautions Avoid during pregnancy. Avoid if you suffer from low blood pressure.

MELISSA
THE HEART OIL

Botanical name
Melissa officinalis

Plant part used Flowering tops and leaves.

Main benefits Melissa calms and soothes the skin (eczema, acne, and insect stings) as well as soothing the mind by calming the nervous system (grief, depression, sadness, and stress). Respiratory-related allergies (hayfever, asthma, and skin reactions) respond well to melissa. Melissa offers relief for problems of the digestive or circulatory system (slows heart palpitations, lowers blood pressure, eases headaches and migraine, calms a persistent cough).

Blending suggestions Its sweet, gentle, lemon aroma blends well with basil, bergamot, chamomile, frankincense, geranium, ginger, lavender, neroli, rosemary, and ylang ylang.

My comment Relax in the bath with 6–8 drops of this calming oil.

Cautions Avoid during pregnancy. There is a risk of allergic reaction due to the high aldehyde content. Use in weaker dilution.

NEROLI
THE MIND, BODY, AND SOUL OIL

Botanical name *Citrus aurantium*

Plant part used Fresh flowers.

Main benefits It helps prevent wrinkles, stretch marks, and thread veins. It has a deep tranquilizing effect and is used for treating anxiety, depression, palpitations, and nervous disorders. The digestive properties of neroli relieve diarrhoea, indigestion, cramps and spasms, and help expel gas from the intestines.

Blending suggestions The exquisite sweet perfume of this oil blends well with most other oils.

My comment Inhale on a tissue or add two drops to your pillow to relieve insomnia.

Cautions Safe and ideal to use during pregnancy.

ORANGE
A CALMING AND RELAXING OIL

Botanical name *Citrus sinensis*

Plant part used Fruit peel.

Main benefits This oil has a refreshing and stimulating effect on the body while still leaving you relaxed. It rejuvenates skin. Excellent oil for calming children as well as for reducing colds and flu. Has antiseptic properties and is useful in the treatment of mouth ulcers.

Blending suggestions The light citrus aroma blends well with cypress, frankincense, lavender, neroli, petitgrain, rose, and rosewood.

My comment Can be added to massage oil for muscle soreness.

Cautions This oil can cause irritation due to photosensitivity. Do not use when pregnant. Do not use within 72 hours of going in the sun.

PATCHOULI
THE GENERAL TONIC OIL

Botanical name *Pogostemon cablin*

Plant part used Dried leaves.

Main benefits Useful in the treatment of eczema, acne, scalp, and fungal infection of the skin. For anxiety and depression, patchouli helps keep you in touch with reality while encouraging spiritual wellbeing.

Blending suggestions The strong, exotic perfume of patchouli blends well with bergamot, clary sage, frankincense, geranium, ginger, lemongrass, neroli, rosewood, rose, sandalwood, and ylang ylang.

My comment Use in facial skin lotion to help reduce wrinkles.

Cautions Safe to use. Non-toxic.

PEPPERMINT
THE SOOTHING DIGESTION OIL

Botanical name *Mentha piperita*

Plant part used Flowering tops and leaves.

Main benefits The cooling and refreshing effect on the body brings temporary relief from headaches, mental fatigue, toothache, sinusitis, travel sickness, sunburn, upset stomachs, and hangovers.

Blending suggestions The strong, pungent, refreshing aroma of peppermint oil blends well with the citrus oils, basil, cypress, eucalyptus, marjoram, pine, rosemary, and thyme.

My comment Improve your concentration by inhaling this oil when at work or studying.

Cautions Avoid during pregnancy. Use with care on sensitive skins—it can be an irritant due to high menthol content.

PETITGRAIN
THE NERVE OIL

Botanical name
Citrus auantium var. *amara*

Plant part used
Leaves from citrus trees.

Main benefits   Petitgrain's
properties include being antidepressant,
deodorizing, and a sedative.

Blending suggestions   Petitgrain's
perfume is sweet and a little sharp.
It blends well with the other citrus oils
as well as clary sage, geranium, and
lavender.

My comment   Use in your oil-warmer
and inhale to reduce depression and to
clear a confused mind.

Cautions   Non-toxic and safe to use at
home.

PINE
THE RESPIRATORY OIL

Botanical name
Pinus sylvestris

Plant part used
Needles, twigs,
and cones.

Main benefits   One of the best oils to
treat head lice, sores, cuts, and scabies.
Pine has a great effect on the respiratory
system and helps to loosen and remove
mucus. Useful in the treatment of
bronchitis, coughs, sore throats, colds,
flu, asthma, and for muscular aches and
pains, arthritis, and rheumatism.

Blending suggestions   The fresh,
clean, camphor smell blends well
with cedarwood, cypress, eucalyptus,
lavender, sweet marjoram, peppermint,
thyme, and tea tree.

My comment   The perfect oil to
benefit the respiratory system. Use in
oil-warmer, bath, and massage oil.

Cautions   It is non-toxic but it can be
an irritant when used in high doses on
sensitive skins. Avoid massage oil and
bathing with pine for allergic skins.

Rose
The beauty oil

Botanical name *Rosa damascene*

Plant part used Petals.

Main benefits Rose oil prevents and reduces scarring. It is a helpful oil for asthma and chronic bronchitis. The beautiful fragrance helps bring balance and harmony as well as stimulating and elevating the mind.

Blending suggestions Blends well with bergamot, chamomile, clary sage, geranium, jasmine, lavender, melissa, rosewood, and ylang ylang.

My comment Use in facial treatments, ideal for all skin types. Use with calendula cream and chamomile for red and inflamed skin.

Cautions Non-toxic and safe to use.

Rosemary
The oil for protection

Botanical name
Rosmarinus officinalis

Plant part used
Flowering top and leaves.

Main benefits Rosemary is a powerful stimulant and has impressive healing properties, strengthening the nervous system, improving memory, and restoring sense of smell. Rosemary can ease the pain of arthritis, gout, rheumatism, stiff and sore muscles. It is also used with success in treating asthma, colds, flu, bronchitis, and coughs.

Blending suggestions The sharp penetrating perfume blends well with basil, cedarwood, all the citrus oils, lavender, and peppermint.

My comment Use regularly as a hair-conditioning rinse. Use also to overcome mental fatigue and improve mental clarity and focus.

Cautions Avoid during pregnancy and if suffering from epilepsy.

Rosewood
A gentle balancing oil

Botanical name
Aniba rosaeodora

Plant part used
Wood from the tropical evergreen tree.

Main benefits Rosewood is soothing, uplifting, refreshing, and balancing. This oil is calming and relaxing for the emotions and gently sensual.

Blending suggestions The sweet, floral, wood aroma blends well with most other essential oils.

My comment Use in facial oils, creams, and lotions, especially for dry and sensitive skins.

Cautions Non-toxic and safe to use.

Tea tree
First aid in a bottle

Botanical name
Melaleuca alternifolia

Plant part used
Leaves and twigs.

Main benefits Tea tree has many outstanding properties. It can be used to treat anything from blisters, boils, burns, rashes, gingivitis, mouth ulcers, burns, insect bites, nappy rash, and ringworm to athlete's foot and thrush, infected wounds, coldsores, corns, and warts.

Blending suggestions The resinous, slightly musty aroma of tea tree blends well with clary sage, cypress, eucalyptus, geranium, ginger, lavender, lemon, lemongrass, rosemary, and thyme.

My comment Use as a gargle for throat and mouth infections.

Cautions Non-toxic and safe to use. Repeated neat application might induce sensitization.

THYME
NATURE'S ANTISEPTIC

Botanical name
Thymus vulgaris

Plant part used Flowering tips and leaves.

Main benefits A powerful healer of skin; a stimulant to the immune and digestive systems; a disinfectant to the respiratory tract; a regulator of menstrual flow and a strengthener to the nervous system.

Blending suggestions The spicy, hot, nutmeg-like aroma blends well with bergamot, cedarwood, eucalyptus, lemon, and rosemary.

My comment Use in the bath, as an inhalation on a tissue, or in a massage oil for relief from cold and flu symptoms.

Cautions Do not use on anyone with high blood pressure. Due to possible irritation factor use in moderation and only well diluted. Avoid during pregnancy.

VETIVER
THE OIL OF TRANQUILITY

Botanical name
Vetiveria zizanioides

Plant part used
Roots of wild grass.

Main benefits One of the best oils to use to strengthen the immune system. It is a deeply relaxing oil. Use in the bath to ease stress, lift depression, calm the nerves, and for insomnia. Its antiseptic properties heal acne, cuts, and infected wounds. Vetiver essential oil can be used during menopause to boost hormone secretions. During pregnancy, this oil improves the tone of slack and tired-looking skin.

Blending suggestions This dark brown, thick oil has an earthy aroma that blends well with clary sage, lavender, geranium, jasmine, patchouli, and ylang ylang.

My comment Use in bath and compress for arthritis and rheumatism.

Cautions Non-toxic, non-irritant. Safe to use.

HOW TO USE ESSENTIAL OILS

Never use essential oils directly on the skin. For safe use, essential oils must always be diluted or diffused as follows:

CARRIER OILS

In carrier oils for massage, friction rub, chest rub, and pulse point application.

AIR

In the air through vaporization, room and car fragrancing, candles, or in the sauna.

WATER

In water for baths, steam inhalation, as a compress, as a gargle/mouthwash, air fresheners, facial sprays, and in the laundry.

NEAT

Neat, as in tissue inhalation, on your pillow, on logs of wood used on the fire, in drawers, cupboards, and in bins.

UNSCENTED BASE CREAMS

In unscented base creams for topical application in creams and lotions.

POWDER

In powder (rice flour or cornstarch) to make foot and body powders.

ALCOHOL

In alcohol to make eau de toilette and perfume.

ESSENTIAL OILS DO NOT DISSOLVE IN WATER BUT DO DISSOLVE IN OIL.

When working with essential oils I recommend you use stainless steel, ceramic, glass, or enamel containers and glass or stainless steel utensils. Do not use plastic bowls or utensils. For cloths or towels I recommend cotton and not synthetic fabrics.

ESSENTIAL OILS IN THE AIR

OIL WARMERS

As essential oils are gently heated in the warmer, the highly volatile oils turn into vapors, and you receive the therapeutic effect by breathing them in the air. One of the most common ways of warming essential oils is to use an electric essential oil warmer.

ELECTRIC OIL WARMER

These are safer than candle warmers, as there is no fire threat with the electric warmer. Place 6–8 drops of pure essential oil in the ceramic indentation and switch on. No water is required in the bowl. To clean the surface, wipe with a clean cloth dipped in pure eucalyptus oil.

CANDLE OIL WARMER

This warmer uses a tea candle and can be a fire hazard. Although they look romantic, you can never be sure of the quality of the candles. Beeswax candles are the best. Add sufficient water to the dish, add 6–8 drops of essential oil, and light the candle. Be sure to keep a check on the water level.

CAR FRESHENERS

Sprinkle a few drops on a tissue/cottonwool ball and place it in the air vent. Basil, peppermint, lemon, and eucalyptus will help keep you alert on a long trip and will also freshen stale air.

CANDLES

Add 2 drops of your chosen essential oil to the melted wax of a candle that has been burning for a short while. The warmth quickly diffuses the aroma into the air. Some essential oils are flammable so blow the candle out when you add the oil and relight the candle with care.

IN A SAUCER

If you do not have an oil warmer, you can put a little water and 6 drops of essential oil in a ceramic/glass saucer, and place it near or just in front of the room heater. The subtle aroma will pervade the air. Alternatively, place a dish of boiling water in a sunny window or in front of the fire and add a few drops of essential oil.

LIGHT BULB RING

This is a circular ring (made of absorbent material) with a hole to fit over a light bulb. Add 3–8 drops of essential oil to the ring and fit over a light bulb.

Diffuse the aroma into the air with candles

ESSENTIAL OILS IN WATER

A hand or foot bath is one of the most effective ways to relieve stress and the next best thing to having an aromatherapy massage. For all water treatments be well prepared and aware of temperature. Dry body brush before a bath.

BATH TIME

A bath reduces tension and anxiety, calms the nervous system, enhances the removal of waste from the body, clears heat, fever, and inflammation, improves circulation of blood and lymph, and reduces pain.

Place 6–8 drops of essential oil in 1 tablespoon carrier oil and add to your full bath. Hop in, swirl the water around and enjoy. Essential oils have a very subtle effect. Do not expect to feel the effect as soon as you lie back— the effect will be felt in the hours that follow.

If you do not have any carrier oil, take a "Cleopatra" bath. Queen Cleopatra bathed in ass's milk. The high-fat content of ass's milk dispersed and diluted the exotic Egyptian oils before touching Cleopatra's beautiful skin.

You can use cream, whole milk, buttermilk, goats' milk, or honey instead of the carrier oil.

A therapeutic bath can help to relieve aches and pains. Make up the bath with up to 2.2 pounds of Epsom salts and 6-8 drops of your chosen essential oils. Stay in the bath for 20 minutes.

A bath reduces tension and anxiety

Be well prepared before you commence

A bath is a pampering treat and promotes good health and wellbeing

Then, dry well and lie flat on your bed, on a large, dry towel, covered with a towel and with another towel cushioning your neck and head.

Cover yourself with a quilt and lie still for 20 minutes. Complete the treatment with an ice-cold shower.

Sauna

Add 3 drops of eucalyptus to the ladle of water you splash onto the coals, or 18 drops to the bucket of water.

Sitzbath

A large bowl or normal bath can be used, filled with enough water to cover your hips. A cold bath, which you sit in for three to five minutes, offers relief for very heavy menstruation. It promotes sound sleep as well as being a preventative measure for colds and flu. A hot sitzbath is comforting for back pain, haemorrhoids, constipation, and urinary problems.

Compress

Soothes aches and pains and relaxes spasms, cramps, and swellings. A hot compress brings increased blood to the area to relieve congestion. Take a small bowl of water and add 10 drops of essential oil. Agitate the water. Fold a clean cloth or towel, immerse in the water, lightly squeeze out excess water, and place on the area. Cover with a blanket or towel to maintain required temperature. When the cloth is at body temperature, reheat or cool as required. Repeat for up to four hours.

Hot compress

For boils, splinters, abscesses, rheumatism, muscular pain, back ache, stomach ache, sore throat, chest congestion, toothache, and menstrual cramps. Always test the temperature of a hot compress before applying.

Also excellent as a weekly hair treatment. Add 5 drops of pure essential oil to one tablespoon of carrier oil (such as avocado oil), massage into scalp, and follow with a hot towel compress.

Cautions A hot compress should never be applied to swollen limbs.

Cold compress

Ideal for sprains, bruises, headaches, burns, sunburn, chicken pox, hangovers, measles, high temperatures, and to relieve inflammation. Leave the compress on for two to four hours. Must be kept moist (add ice blocks to the water).

Warm compress

Good for skin treatments. When pure essential oils are used on the face in massage or an oil mask, the warm compress is used to infuse the oils into the skin.

Cautions Avoid the eye area when administering a face compress.

Hot and cold compress

Alternating hot and cold water is good for arthritis and infections.

Steam inhalation

Ideal for treating coughs and colds and for a steam facial. Place 1 quart of steaming hot water in a bowl. Add 5 drops of essential oil to the water. Bend forward over the bowl and drape a large towel over your head to trap the vapors. Inhale. Add some more boiling water to evaporate off any remaining essential oils.

Gargle/mouthwash

Treat halitosis, a sore throat, or toothache. Add 2 drops of tea tree essential oil and 1 teaspoon of salt to a glass of warm water. Stir until salt is dissolved. Gargle every hour until symptoms are reduced. When gargling, keep the solution in the mouth/throat for as long as possible before spitting out. Do not swallow.

Spritz—facial spray

Floral waters are best made using de-ionized or distilled water, or bottled spring water. Simply add 15 drops of essential oil to 1½ fl oz of water. Hydrates and freshens the skin.

Spritz—air freshener

Add 50 drops of essential oil to a 16 fl oz spray bottle for a natural, non-aerosol spray to deodorize and perfume a room.

Spritz—insect repellent

Mix 40 drops of essential oil to 4 fl oz of water. Use a pump spray bottle. Shake well before spraying into the air, onto your clothes, or where insects scuttle.

Laundry rinse

Add 3 drops of essential oil to final rinse water.

Suggested oils

Steam inhalation
- Eucalyptus, peppermint, thyme, tea tree for chest, nasal, and sinus problems.
- Lavender for headaches
- Sandalwood, frankincense, geranium for facial steams (use only 2 drops pure essential oil)

Gargle/mouthwash
- Tea tree, eucalyptus, vetiver, thyme, and peppermint all contain compounds clinically proven to kill bacteria that cause bad breath, plaque, and gum disease such as gingivitis.

Note: If you are suffering from toothache, make an appointment to see your dentist as soon as possible.

Spritz—facial spray
- For normal skin:
  Geranium and lavender
- For dry skin:
  Sandalwood and frankincense
- For oily skin:
  Cypress and lemon
- For blemished and sensitive skins:
  Chamomile and geranium

Spritz—air freshener
- Lavender to kill airborne germs.
- Peppermint to remove the stale smell of cigarettes.
- Lemon or lime for cooking smells.
- Pine, rosemary, or lavender for disinfecting.

Spritz—insect repellant
- Camphor for moths.
- Citronella or lemongrass for mosquitoes and flying insects.
- Tea tree or peppermint for ants and fleas.
- Eucalyptus for cockroaches.

Laundry rinse
- Lemon and eucalyptus

TREATING COMMON AILMENTS

Essential oils assist the body to heal itself by lowering stress levels, relaxing and toning the muscles and stimulating the immune system, the organs and the glands in the body. Oils can be used to relieve symptoms and help the natural healing of everyday ailments.

See the reference chart for common ailments, showing which oils to choose and the application method suggested. Check the guidelines when using essential oils (page 9) and relevant cautions before preparing the remedy.

Be sure that you are only treating common problems. If symptoms are severe, or continue, please seek consultation with your naturopath or health care professional.

COMPLEMENTARY THERAPY

Aromatherapy is a complementary therapy and needs to go hand-in-hand with the following lifestyle checks to be fully effective:

- Diet correction
- Regular exercise
- Drink 2 liters of water per day
- Cut coffee completely from your diet
- Reduce alcohol consumption

- Have enough quality sleep every day
- Reduce stress wherever possible.

Last, but by no means least, correct the balance in your life between work life, home life, and spiritual life, and include time for relaxation.

TREATMENTS—ABBREVIATIONS

aM	Abdomen massage	hG	Hot gargle/mouthwash
B	Bath	icC	Ice cold compress
C	Compress	L	Lotion
cC	Cold compress	M	Massage
cM	Chest massage	N	Neat
CR	Cream	P	Perfume
CWB	Cottonwool balls	PP	Pulse point massage
fB	Footbath	rS	Room spray
FM	Face massage	SB	Skin brushing
fR	Friction rub massage	sB	Sitz bath
hB	Hand bath	sI	Steam inhalation
hC	Hot compress	sM	Scalp massage
h&cC	Hot and cold compress	sS	Spritz facial spray
h&fB	Hand and footbath	ThB	Therapeutic bath
h&M	Hand and foot massage	tI	Tissue inhalation

ESSENTIAL OILS FOR COMMON AILMENTS

Common Ailments	Helpful Pure Essential Oil	Method of Application
Abdominal pain	Peppermint, chamomile, marjoram, fennel	M B
Abscesses	Lavender, tea tree, chamomile	hC
Dental abscess	Tea tree, lavender	hG
Acne	Patchouli, lavender, roman chamomile, geranium	FM
Anxiety and stress	Basil, sandalwood, bergamot, frankincense, cypress, lavender, neroli, patchouli, orange, rose	B M tI P PP
Arthritis and rheumatism	Cypress, fennel, lemon, ginger, frankincense, eucalyptus, pine, lavender, pine, rosemary	ThB sI M b&c
Athletes foot	Tea tree, lavender, geranium, patchouli	fB
Backache	Chamomile, lavender and frankincense	M B
Bilious attack	Rosemary, fennel	N
Black eye	Lavender	cC
Bleeding (external)	Geranium, lemon, chamomile, cypress	icC
Blisters	Chamomile, lavender	N sS icC
Broken capillaries	Chamomile, cypress, rose, lavender, lemon	B M C
Bruises	Lavender, fennel, geranium, cypress	M icC
Bunions	Chamomile, melissa, peppermint, lavender, cypress, lemon	fB M b&c
Burns	Lavender	N sS icC
Cellulite	Cypress, lavender, fennel, geranium, grapefruit, rosemary	M SB
Chapped lips	Chamomile, geranium	CR
Circulation and chilblains	Cypress, ginger, rosemary, marjoram, eucalyptus, geranium, lavender	b&c
Colds and flu	Lemon, eucalyptus, tea tree, pine, thyme	ThB rS tI sI
Coldsore (herpes)	Melissa, bergamot, geranium, lavender, tea tree and patchouli	N C L
Constipation & digestive problems	Rosemary, lemon, peppermint, lemongrass, orange (slow digestion)	C aM
Corns	Lemon	N
Coughs	Eucalyptus, thyme	sI cM
Cystitis	Sandalwood, bergamot, tea tree	aM sB
Dandruff	Cedarwood, lavender, rosemary, geranium, tea tree, sandalwood	hC sM
Dermatitis and psoriasis	Frankincense, chamomile, geranium, lavender, rosewood and bergamot	B M C L CR

Ailment	Oils	Methods
Earache	Chamomile, lavender, tea tree	CWB B M C L CR
Eczema (dry)	Chamomile, geranium, patchouli	B C L CR
Eczema (weeping)	Bergamot, juniper, melissa	B fB tl
Fatigue	Geranium, peppermint, rosemary, basil, clary sage	C L ThB
Fluid retention	Cypress, fennel, grapefruit, juniper, geranium, bergamot	N
Foot blisters	Chamomile, lavender, tea tree	
Fungal infection (eg: tinea)	Geranium, lemongrass, tea tree, lavender, patchouli	fB P L C
Haemorrhoids	Patchouli, geranium, chamomile	C sB
Hair loss	Lavender, rosemary, clary sage, ylang ylang	sM
Halitosis	Peppermint, lemon, tea tree, lavender and thyme	hG
Hay fever	Chamomile, lemon, lavender	sl P PP
Headaches	Lavender, lemongrass, marjoram, peppermint, rose, rosewood, vetiver	P PP
Hiccups	Lavender, lemon	fR tl M *(throat, solar plexus, and abdomen)*
High blood pressure	Lemon	M
Indigestion	Peppermint, ginger, lemongrass	aM
Insomnia	Lavender, orange, lemon, mandarin, rose, sandalwood, vetiver, ylang ylang, geranium, neroli, jasmine	tl M B
Itching skin	Chamomile, cedarwood, bergamot, lavender, patchouli, lime	B M L
Mosquito repellent	Eucalyptus, peppermint, citronella, geranium	rS L
Muscular aches	Rosemary, eucalyptus, basil, lavender, clary sage	M B C
Muscular stiffness	Rosemary, neroli, melissa, cypress, peppermint	M B C
Muscular tone	Lavender, lemongrass, marjoram, neroli	M B C
Nausea	Peppermint, basil, fennel, ginger	M sl
PMT	Clary sage, orange, lemon, chamomile, geranium, neroli, mandarin	M B
Respiratory congestion	Rosemary, eucalyptus, frankincense, pine, chamomile, patchouli	M tl
Shingles	Geranium, bergamot, chamomile	N C
Sinusitis	Rosemary, eucalyptus, peppermint, lemon, pine	sl P PP
Smelly feet	Cedarwood, cypress, citronella	P fB CWB *(in shoes)*
Snoring	Thyme	fR
Sore throat	Eucalyptus, lime, tea tree, thyme, frankincense	sl M hG *(throat and neck)*
Sprains	Eucalyptus, chamomile, lavender	C
Sunburn	Lavender, peppermint, tea tree, chamomile	sS cC *(on head)*
Toothache	Chamomile, lemon, peppermint, tea tree	hG
Varicose veins	Cypress, lemon, rosemary, lavender, geranium	M C B
Warts	Lemon, lavender	N

ABOUT THE AUTHOR

MARGIE HARE was born in Cape Town, South Africa. She was a speech and drama teacher then a publishing sales executive before establishing her own business specializing in growing and marketing herbs. An intense interest in the therapeutic power of herbs led Margie to study other alternative-healing therapies, including aromatherapy, reflexology, and massage. In 1994, she won the prestigious Herb Woman of the Year award for education in the field of herbs and healing. During this time, she was herb consultant and lecturer at one of South Africa's leading health resorts, Stellenbosch Hydro. In 1996, Margie moved to Australia as a marketing executive with a wine company, but was soon managing her own alternative-health business, Divine Touch. She now practices as a holistic healing therapist in aromatherapy, reflexology, Dr Vodder Manual Lymph Drainage, and combined decongestive therapy, remedial massage, Reiki, and crystal point therapy. Margie is also a consultant and lecturer at Hopewood Health Centre, one of Australia's top health retreats. She is a member of the Australasian Vodder Therapists Association (AVTA) and Remedial Masseurs Association (RMA), and president of the North Sydney chapter of Business Network International, a global business-marketing organization.

Divine Touch

"Massage tailored to balance your body"

www.divinearomatherapy.com.au